MAKE AND CREATE
GLASS PAINTING
AND
FUNKY FABRICS

Written by Susie Hodge

Photography by Calvey Taylor-Haw

Craftwork by Ana Bjezancevic

Published by Top That! Publishing plc
Tide Mill Way, Woodbridge, Suffolk, IP12 1AP, UK
www.topthatpublishing.com
Copyright © 2013 Top That! Publishing plc

Glass Painting
Getting Started

The following pages are full of exciting projects for you to make using glass paints. There are all kinds of projects, from large to small, arty to useful, and for you to make for yourself or to give as gifts. Each of the projects has illustrated step-by-step instructions to make creative glass paint designs fun and easy!

GLASS PAINTS

There are many different types of glass paints, and some are better for specific jobs. However, to get started, and complete the projects on the following pages, you will need a black outliner paint, a range of coloured glass paints and a rubber-ended spreading tool, or 'smoothing stick', to guide lines and spread the paint.

OTHER MATERIALS

It is useful to keep a sketch pad close so you can practise the designs or work out some of your own ideas. Most projects require a few other materials, such as a pencil, permanent marker and newspaper to protect your work surface. Before you begin, make sure that you have all the materials you need.

After you have finished your project, remember to clean the nozzle of the paint tube, replace the cap and leave your work to dry in a safe place.

PAINTING TECHNIQUES

Two glass painting techniques are used in this book. You can use whichever technique you prefer – they both work for all the projects! However, you might find one method easier to use than the other depending on the project or the item you are decorating.

DIRECT TECHNIQUE

Direct painting is useful when you have a flat surface to work on.
- First, mark the outline of your design on to your item with a permanent marker. Then use the black outliner to follow the lines of your pen. The pointed end of a smoothing stick can help to guide your lines.

- When the black outline has completely dried, spread the coloured paint inside the outlines.

- Use the flat end of a smoothing stick to blend and spread the coloured paints.

ACETATE TECHNIQUE

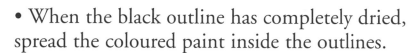

A piece of acetate is used as a base, which is painted onto directly.
- First, use the black outliner to draw the outlines of your design. Place the acetate over a sketch pad design and trace it if you find it easier.

- When the outlines are completely dry, spread the coloured paints inside them. Use the smoothing stick to blend and smooth the coloured paints.

- Once the paint has dried, peel the design off the acetate. While tacky, stick it firmly to the surface of the item you are using for your project. Make sure that there are no gaps in your black outlines or coloured paints so the paint is less likely to tear when peeled.

Be careful!
Ask an adult to help you with any tricky bits. Ask for an adult's permission before you customise any glass items. Work on a firm surface and be extremely careful when handling glass.

Cosmic Candleholders

These celestial candleholders make a good present for an adult at festive times of the year. This project uses the acetate method.

YOU WILL NEED:

- a pencil
- a sketch pad
- old newspaper
- acetate
- black paint outliner
- a smoothing stick
- coloured glass paints
- a pair of candleholders
- two candles

1. Using a pencil and a sketch pad, try out some decorative designs. Have a go at several different ideas or follow the designs on this page. Think of celestial ideas – try stars, planets or zodiac signs.

2. Cover your work surface with old newspaper to protect it. Place a piece of acetate over your designs on the sketch pad. Trace the drawings from the sketch pad onto the acetate with black outliner. Guide the paint with a smoothing stick. Allow the paint to dry.

3. When the outlines are completely dry, begin filling in the spaces with colour. Spread the paint with the smoothing stick to gently push and expand the colours. Make sure that they really do fill the outlines with no gaps.

4. When the paints are completely dry, peel each design off the acetate and choose where you are going to apply the decorations to the candleholders.

5. Stick the designs onto the candleholders, pressing them down firmly.

6. Ask an adult to light the candles and watch your cosmic candleholders sparkle! Never leave the candles unattended.

Tip: Using the flat end of a smoothing stick helps to spread the colours. You will find this helps to cover up any gaps you might have left.

Top Jar!

This is a useful jar that you can keep all sorts of things in, or make as a gift for someone else. This project uses the acetate method.

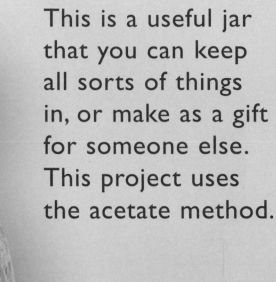

YOU WILL NEED:
- a pencil
- a sketch pad
- old newspaper
- acetate
- black paint outliner
- a smoothing stick
- coloured glass paints
- a glass jar
- a piece of felt (large enough to cover the jar lid)
- PVA glue

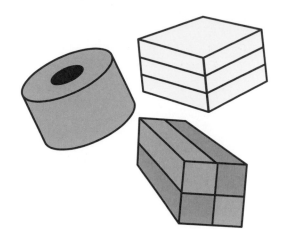

1. Using a pencil and a sketch pad, try out some decorative designs. Have a go at several different ideas or follow the designs on this page. Think about what you will use the jar for – maybe sweets, teabags, coffee or bath salts – as this might affect your choice of decoration.

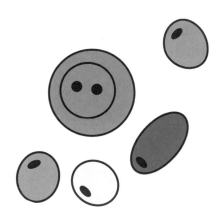

2. Cover your work surface with old newspaper to protect it. Place a piece of acetate over the sketch pad. Trace the drawings from the sketch pad onto the acetate carefully with black paint outliner. Guide the paint with a smoothing stick. Allow the paint to dry.

3. When the outlines are completely dry, begin filling in the spaces with colour. Smooth the paint with the smoothing stick to gently push and expand the colours. Make sure that they really do fill the outlines with no gaps.

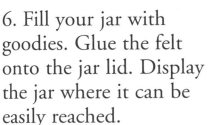

4. When the paints are completely dry, peel each design off the acetate and choose where you are going to apply the decorations on the jar.

5. Stick the designs onto the jar, pressing them down firmly.

6. Fill your jar with goodies. Glue the felt onto the jar lid. Display the jar where it can be easily reached.

Tip: You could ask an adult to make a money slot in the jar lid and use it as a money box.

Flower Vase

Here you can have flowers on a vase, not just in it! This project uses the acetate method.

YOU WILL NEED:
- a pencil
- a sketch pad
- old newspaper
- acetate
- black paint outliner
- a smoothing stick
- coloured glass paints
- a plain glass vase

4. When the paints are completely dry, peel each design off the acetate and choose where you are going to apply the decorations on the vase.

5. Stick the designs onto the vase, pressing them down firmly.

6. Fill your vase with real flowers for a beautiful display!

1. Using a pencil and a sketch pad, try out some decorative flower designs. Have a go at several different ideas or follow the designs on this page.

2. Cover your work surface with old newspaper to protect it. Place a piece of acetate over the sketch pad. Trace the drawings from the sketch pad onto the acetate with black paint outliner. Guide the paint with a smoothing stick. Allow the paint to dry.

3. When the outlines are dry, begin filling in the spaces with colour. Spread the paint with the smoothing stick to gently push and expand the colours. Make sure that they really do fill the outlines with no gaps.

Tip: It is best to use the flat acetate technique for decorating a curved surface, otherwise the paint may run before it has dried!

Magical Mirror

This magical mirror will reflect the light and cheer up any room! This project uses the direct painting method.

1. Using a pencil and sketch pad, try out some decorative designs. Have a go at several different ideas or follow the designs on this page. You may find it best to keep your decorations in a corner or along the edge of the mirror so you can still see yourself in it.

2. Draw your chosen design onto the mirror using a permanent marker pen.

4. When the outlines are completely dry, begin filling in the spaces with colour. Spread the paint with the smoothing stick to gently push and expand the colours. Leave it to dry.

5. Admire your work whenever you look at yourself in the mirror!

3. Cover your work surface with old newspaper to protect it. Following your guidelines, lightly and carefully apply black paint outliner to the mirror. Guide the paint with a smoothing stick. Allow the paint to dry.

Tip: It is easy to smudge the paint while it is wet, so be careful of where you move your hand as you work.

Wonderful Windows

Try painting a window to brighten up a room! You could start with one design and end up with lots of different designs on your window. This project uses the acetate method.

YOU WILL NEED:
- a pencil
- a sketch pad
- old newspaper
- acetate
- black paint outliner
- a smoothing stick
- coloured glass paints
- a window

1. Using a pencil and a sketch pad, try out some decorative designs. Have a go at several different ideas or follow the designs you see here. A butterfly or dragonfly makes a very attractive window decoration.

2. Cover your work surface with old newspaper to protect it. Place a piece of acetate over the sketch pad. Trace the drawings from the sketch pad onto the acetate with black paint outliner. Guide the paint with a smoothing stick. Allow the paint to dry.

3. When the outlines are completely dry, begin filling in the spaces with colour. Smooth the paint with the smoothing stick to gently push and expand the colours. Make sure that they really do fill the outlines with no gaps.

4. When the paints are completely dry, peel the design off the acetate and choose where you are going to apply the decoration on the window.

5. Stick the design onto the window, pressing it down firmly.

6. When you have completed your window, stand back and admire it.

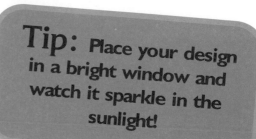

Tip: Place your design in a bright window and watch it sparkle in the sunlight!

Fairy Pencil Case

Customise your pencil case – and make it as individual as you are! This project uses the direct painting method.

4. When the outlines are completely dry, begin filling in the spaces with colour. Smooth the paint with the smoothing stick to gently push and spread the colours. Leave it to dry.

5. When you take your pencil case into school, everyone will want one just like it!

1. Using a pencil and a sketch pad, try out some decorative designs. Have a go at several different ideas or follow the designs you see on this page. You can make your decoration as simple or as complicated as you wish. Try one large design, or lots of small designs.

2. Lay your pencil case on your sketch pad and trace your chosen design onto the pencil case using a marker pen.

3. Cover your work surface with old newspaper to protect it. Following your guidelines, lightly and carefully apply black paint outliner to the pencil case. Guide the paint with a smoothing stick. Allow the paint to dry.

Tip: Work on both sides of your pencil case if you wish, but make sure that the paint is completely dry before turning it over.

Funky Fabrics
Getting Started

There are lots of exciting projects for you to make using fabric paints. Each project includes easy-to-follow, step-by-step instructions to create a whole range of funky fabrics!

FABRIC PAINTS

To create the projects on the following pages you will need a range of coloured fabric paints and a smoothing stick. Fabric paint is versatile and easy to use. It is made up of pigment, which gives it its colour, and glue, which makes it stick to the fabric. Fabric paints can be used on almost any type of material, although natural fibres are best. You can buy fabric paints in transparent sparkly colours and opaque colours in craft or hobby shops or online.

OTHER MATERIALS

Keep a sketch pad close when you are creating the projects so you can practise the designs or work out some of your own ideas. In addition to fabric paints, a smoothing stick and sketch pad, you will need chalk or a pencil to draw or mark your design on your chosen fabric and old newspaper to protect your working surface. While working, a piece of cardboard placed inside a garment stops the paint seeping through to the back. After you have finished using the paints, wipe clean the nozzle of the paint tube, replace the cap and leave your work to dry in a safe place.

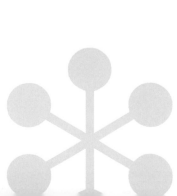

PAINTING TECHNIQUES

• First, copy the design from your sketch book onto the fabric, using chalk or pencil.

• Apply the paint carefully onto your fabric within your chalk lines. When applying the paints, start at the bottom of your garment, resting your working hand on your work surface so that it  doesn't wobble as you work. Move the paint in one direction so you don't smudge your design and try not to stretch the fabric as you go.

• Smooth the paint using a smoothing stick. Try not to blend the colours together or they will turn a sludgy colour.

LOOKING AFTER YOUR FABRIC

When you have finished painting, leave the fabric to dry overnight. The items or garments you have made can be washed and ironed after they have dried, although all items decorated with fabric paint should be hand washed at a cool temperature.

> ## Be careful! ⚠
> For all the projects you will need an adult to help you. Fabric paints won't come off, so be sure that you check first that the garments you are using can be customised.

Flower T-shirt

Decorate your own clothes with fabric paint! Personalise a plain T-shirt by creating your own flower design.

YOU WILL NEED:

- a pencil
- a sketch pad
- a pale-coloured T-shirt
- pencil or chalk
- old newspaper
- cardboard
- fabric paints
- a smoothing stick

1. Using a pencil and sketch pad, create some flower designs. Have a go at several different ideas, or follow the designs on this page.

2. When you are happy with your designs, place your T-shirt on a table or another firm surface. Now decide where you will draw your design on the T-shirt – perhaps on the sleeve, near the neck, in the middle or on the back.

3. Carefully mark your flower design onto the T-shirt using the pencil or chalk.

4. When you are satisfied with your outlines, cover your work surface with old newspaper to protect it. Place some cardboard inside your T-shirt, underneath the part you are going to paint. Carefully paint on the different colours following the outlines of the design.

5. Smooth the paint onto your design with a smoothing stick and gently push and spread the colours carefully inside your outlines, without overlapping.

6. Leave your T-shirt to dry overnight, making sure it is lying flat. Remove the cardboard from inside and get ready to show off your new-look T-shirt!

Tip: As well as different designs, think about using a range of colours.

Animal Crackers Cap

This is one cool cap and you'll be the envy of your friends when you wear it! Decorate it with your favourite animals.

YOU WILL NEED:
- a pencil
- a sketch pad
- a pale-coloured cap
- pencil or chalk
- old newspaper
- fabric paints
- a smoothing stick

1. Using a pencil and sketch pad, create some animal designs. Have a go at several different ideas, try drawing your favourite animals or follow the designs on this page. Think about your favourite animals in the wild as well as pets at home.

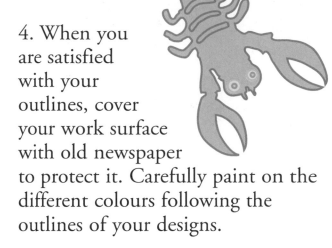

4. When you are satisfied with your outlines, cover your work surface with old newspaper to protect it. Carefully paint on the different colours following the outlines of your designs.

5. Smooth the paint onto your design with a smoothing stick and gently push and spread the colours carefully inside your outlines, without overlapping.

6. Leave your cap to dry overnight, making sure it is lying flat. Wear your cap whatever the weather – rain, sun, snow or wind!

2. When you are happy with your designs, put your cap on a table or other firm surface. Now choose where you are going to decorate your cap – perhaps on the front, the back or on the peak.

3. Carefully mark your designs onto the cap using the pencil or chalk.

Tip: You may find it easier to paint on the cap if you stuff it with newspaper first.

Shapes Cushion

Decorate a cushion with fun shapes or make your shapes into a pattern. You could place them in the centre, just in one corner or all over. It's up to you!

YOU WILL NEED:

- a pencil
- a sketch pad
- a pale-coloured cushion with removable cover
- pencil or chalk
- old newspaper
- cardboard
- fabric paints
- a smoothing stick

1. Using a pencil and sketch pad, try drawing some different shapes. Try some simple geometric shapes, alphabet letters or follow the simple designs you see on this page.

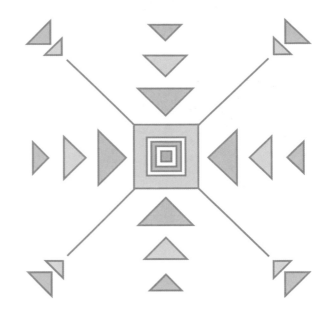

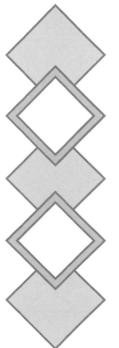

2. When you are happy with your pattern, remove the cover from the cushion. Put the cover on a table or other firm surface. Now choose which part of the cushion you are going to decorate – all over if you want!

3. Carefully mark your designs on the cushion with the pencil or chalk.

4. When you are satisfied with your outlines, cover your work surface with old newspaper to protect it. Place some cardboard inside the cushion cover, underneath the part you are going to paint. Carefully paint on the different colours following the outlines of your designs.

5. Smooth the paint onto your design with a smoothing stick and gently push and spread the colours carefully inside your outlines, without overlapping.

6. When the cushion cover is dry, remove the cardboard and put the cushion back inside the cover. It's ready to display!

Tip: If you are not confident in your drawing skills, try tracing any of the designs onto your fabric.

Jazzy Jeans

Your jeans need never be boring again! Perhaps try a design with flowers along the legs of your jeans, or try decorating the back pockets.

YOU WILL NEED:

- a pencil
- a sketch pad
- pale-coloured denim jeans
- pencil or chalk
- old newspaper
- cardboard
- fabric paints
- a smoothing stick

1. Using a pencil and sketch pad, draw some jazzy designs. Have a go at several different ideas, or follow the designs on this page.

2. When you are happy with your designs, put your jeans on a table or other firm surface. Now decide where you are going to decorate your jeans – on the leg, pockets, around the ankle – wherever!

3. Carefully mark your cool designs on the jeans with the pencil or chalk.

4. When you are satisfied with your outlines, cover your work surface with newspaper to protect it. Place some cardboard inside the jeans, underneath the part you are going to paint. Carefully paint on the different colours following the outlines of your design.

5. Smooth the paint onto your design with a smoothing stick and gently push and spread the colours carefully inside your outlines, without overlapping.

6. Leave your jeans to dry overnight, making sure they are lying flat. Remove the cardboard from inside and hang them up away from direct heat. Wear your jazzy jeans when you want to look cool!

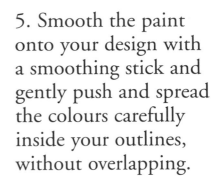

Tip: You might want to begin with just a few designs round the bottom of the trouser legs to see how this turns out, and then add more designs later.

Personalised Pencil Case

When you personalise your pencil case, you could find yourself being asked to help design all your friends' pencil cases too!

1. Using a pencil and sketch pad, create some personal designs. If you like pop music, you could try drawing a guitar and musical notes. Have a go at several different ideas, or follow the designs you see on this page.

2. When you arc happy with your designs, put your pencil case on a table or other firm surface. Now choose which parts you are going to decorate – all over or just in certain areas.

3. Carefully mark your designs on the pencil case with the pencil or chalk.

4. When you are satisfied with your outlines, cover your work surface with old newspaper to protect it. Place some cardboard inside the pencil case underneath the part you are going to paint.

Keeping the pencil case flat as you work, carefully paint on the different colours following the outlines of the designs.

5. Smooth the paint onto your design with a smoothing stick and gently push and spread the colours carefully inside your outlines, without overlapping.

6. Leave your pencil case to dry overnight. Remove the cardboard and put your pens and pencils inside. You now own a pencil case that is completely unique!

Tip: Don't paint on the fastening of the pencil case or it might be difficult to open and close it!

Star Bag

YOU WILL NEED:
- a pencil
- a sketch pad
- pencil or chalk
- a light-coloured bag
- cardboard
- fabric paints
- a smoothing stick
- sequins and beads (optional)

Jazz up a little bag with a design for star quality! This bag is just the right accessory for when you want to dress up.

1. Using a pencil and sketch pad, create some star-shaped designs. Have a go at several different ideas, or follow some of the designs on this page.

2. Once you are happy with your designs, put your bag on a table or other firm surface. Now choose which part of the bag you are going to decorate.

3. Carefully mark your designs on the bag with the pencil or chalk.

4. When you are happy with your outlines, cover your work surface with old newspaper to protect it. Place some cardboard underneath the part you are going to paint. Carefully apply the fabric paint to your bag, following your designs.

5. Smooth the paint onto your design with a smoothing stick and gently push and spread the colours carefully inside your outlines without overlapping.

6. Leave your bag to dry overnight. Your bag will sparkle as you carry it around with you. It may even start a trend among your friends!

Tip: Add extra sparkle to your bag by sewing on shining beads and sequins.

Chic Sandals

All of your friends will want a pair of these cool sandals. You can make them as individual as you like with your own different designs.

5. Smooth the paint onto your design with a smoothing stick and gently push and spread the colours carefully inside your outlines, without overlapping.

6. When you have finished, leave your sandals somewhere warm and dry, but away from direct heat, so that they dry fully, preferably overnight. Then go and show off your shoes!

1. Using a pencil and sketch pad, create some chic designs. Have a go at several different ideas, or follow the designs on this page.

2. When you are happy with your designs, put your sandals on a table or other firm surface. Now choose where the designs would fit and look best.

3. Carefully mark your designs on the sandals with the pencil or chalk.

4. When you are satisfied with your outlines, cover your work surface with old newspaper to protect it. Carefully paint on the different colours following the outlines of your designs.

Tip: Less is more! Don't overdo the designs – you can always add more, but you can't take away paint once it's there.

Further Ideas

Once you've made all of the cool glass paintings and funky fabric designs included in this book, you will be a pro and ready to start designing your own amazing designs on glass and fabric!

Begin by planning your designs on a sketch pad as you have been doing so far. For inspiration, look all around you. All sorts of patterns or markings from plants, animals or materials could be used and adapted for creative effects. Think as well about products to match items you have already created – try a hairband to match your star bag, or decorate glasses to complement your flower vase.

Whatever you decide to do, remember the key is patience – a beautiful design can be ruined by rushing or smudging the paints.

The possibilities are endless!